Who is Under There?

written by Jay Dale

illustrated by Philip Webb

Grandma has an old cat.

On Monday, there was
a big BANG under the house.

"Grandma," said Tina.
"Who is under there?"

"It is our cat," said Grandma.

So under the house she went.
"We were looking for you!" she said.

Grandma has an old dog.

On Tuesday, there was
a big BANG under the house.

"Grandma," said Tina.
"Who is under there?"

"It is our dog," said Grandma.

So under the house she went.
"We were looking for you!" she said.

Grandma has an old cow.

On Wednesday, there was
a big BANG under the house.

"Grandma," said Tina.
"Who is under there?"

"It is our cow," said Grandma.

So under the house she went.
"We were looking for you!" she said.

Grandma has an old horse.

On Thursday, there was
a big BANG under the house.

"Grandma," said Tina
"Who is under there?"

"It is our horse," said Grandma.

So under the house she went.
"We were looking for you!" she said.

On Friday, there was
no bang under the house.

On Saturday, there was
no bang under the house.

Friday
8
May

Saturday
9
May

But on Sunday, there was
a **BIG BANG** under the house.

"Oh, no!" said Tina.
"Who can it be?
It is not our cat.
It is not our dog.
It is not our cow.
It is not our horse.
Who is under there?"

13

"It is our elephant!" said Grandma.
"We were looking for you!"